SESSIO

Campaign

GM

Volume 1

SESSION

Game Date: _____

World Date: _____

Pregame

☐ _____ ☐ _____
☐ _____ ☐ _____
☐ _____ ☐ _____

Session Notes

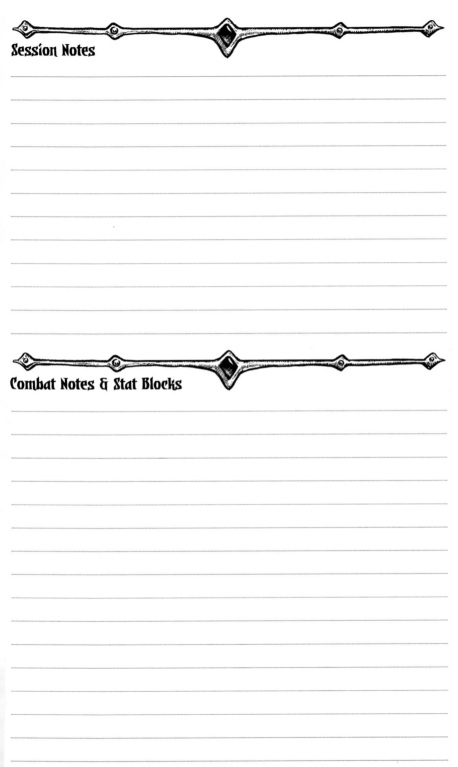

Session Notes

Combat Notes & Stat Blocks

SESSION

Game Date: _____

World Date: _____

Pregame

☐ _____   ☐ _____

☐ _____   ☐ _____

☐ _____   ☐ _____

Session Notes

Session Notes

Combat Notes & Stat Blocks

SESSION

Game Date: _____

World Date: _____

Pregame

☐ _____   ☐ _____

☐ _____   ☐ _____

☐ _____   ☐ _____

Session Notes

_____

_____

_____

_____

_____

_____

_____

_____

_____

_____

_____

_____

_____

_____

_____

_____

_____

_____

_____

_____

_____

_____

_____

_____

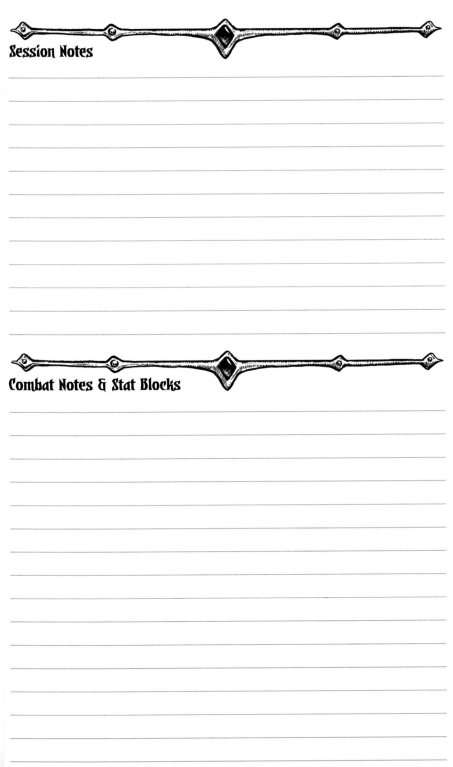

Session Notes

Combat Notes & Stat Blocks

SESSION

Game Date: _____

World Date: _____

Pregame

☐ _____   ☐ _____

☐ _____   ☐ _____

☐ _____   ☐ _____

Session Notes

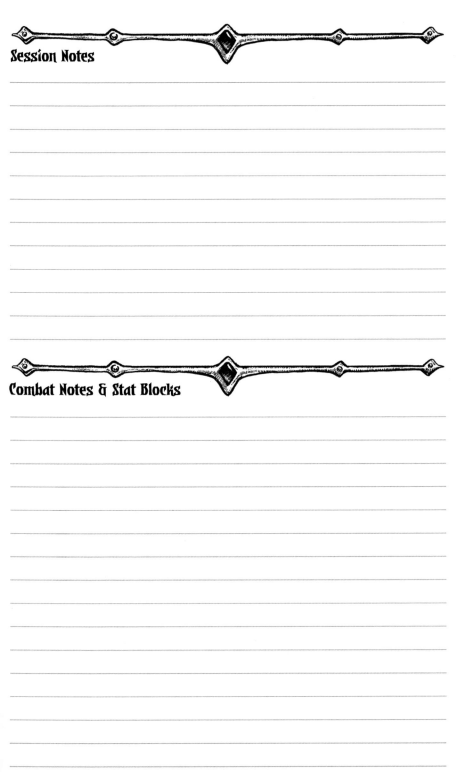

Session Notes

Combat Notes & Stat Blocks

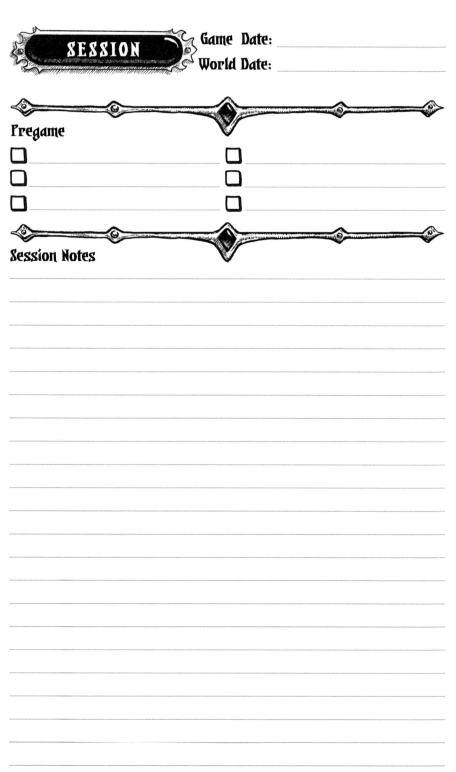

SESSION

Game Date: _____

World Date: _____

Pregame

☐ _____   ☐ _____

☐ _____   ☐ _____

☐ _____   ☐ _____

Session Notes

_____

_____

_____

_____

_____

_____

_____

_____

_____

_____

_____

_____

_____

_____

_____

_____

_____

_____

_____

_____

_____

_____

_____

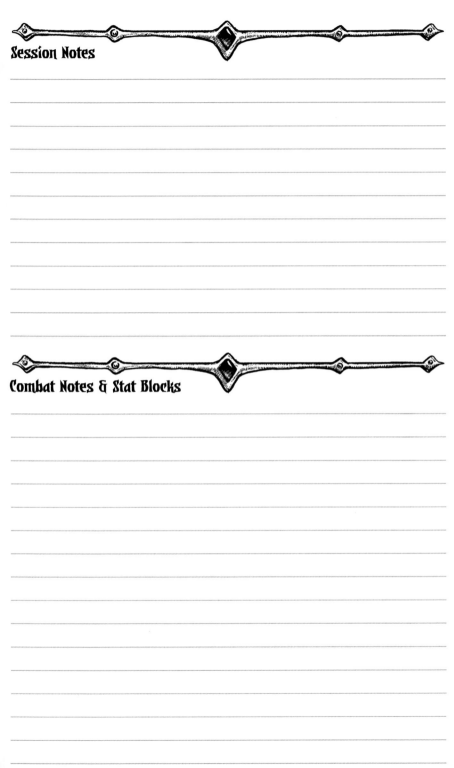

Session Notes

Combat Notes & Stat Blocks

SESSION

Game Date: _____
World Date: _____

Pregame

- [ ] _____
- [ ] _____
- [ ] _____
- [ ] _____
- [ ] _____
- [ ] _____

Session Notes

_____
_____
_____
_____
_____
_____
_____
_____
_____
_____
_____
_____
_____
_____
_____
_____
_____
_____
_____
_____
_____
_____
_____

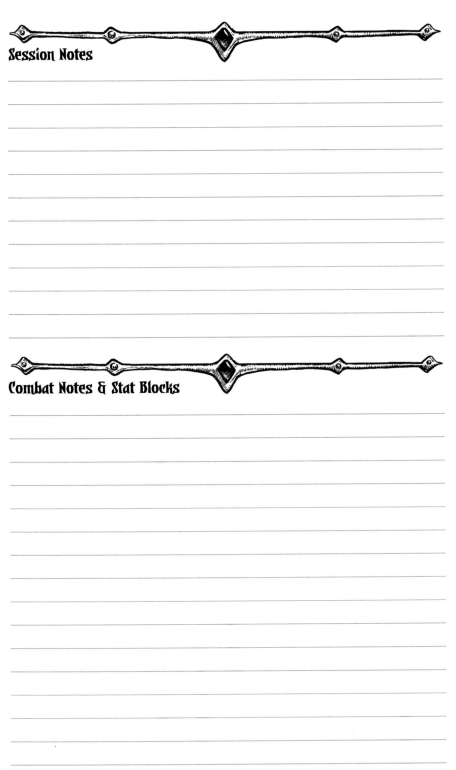

Session Notes

Combat Notes & Stat Blocks

SESSION

Game Date: _____

World Date: _____

Pregame

☐ _____ ☐ _____

☐ _____ ☐ _____

☐ _____ ☐ _____

Session Notes

_____

_____

_____

_____

_____

_____

_____

_____

_____

_____

_____

_____

_____

_____

_____

_____

_____

_____

_____

_____

_____

_____

_____

_____

Session Notes

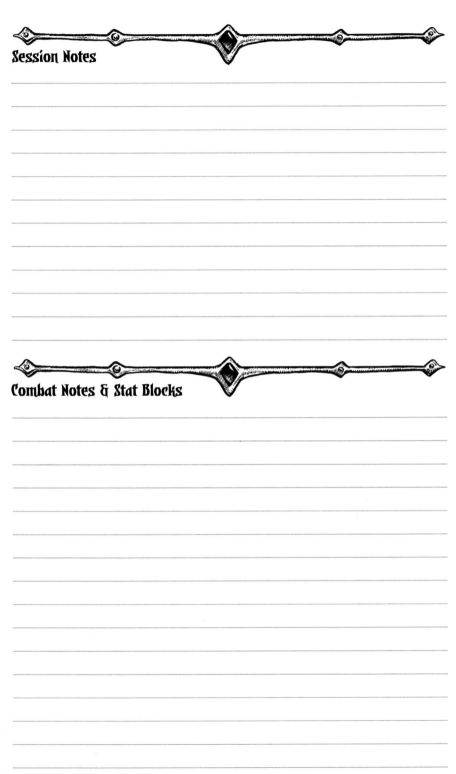

Combat Notes & Stat Blocks

SESSION

Game Date: _____

World Date: _____

Pregame

☐ _____   ☐ _____

☐ _____   ☐ _____

☐ _____   ☐ _____

Session Notes

_____

_____

_____

_____

_____

_____

_____

_____

_____

_____

_____

_____

_____

_____

_____

_____

_____

_____

_____

_____

_____

_____

_____

_____

Session Notes

Combat Notes & Stat Blocks

SESSION

Game Date: _____

World Date: _____

Pregame

☐ _____   ☐ _____

☐ _____   ☐ _____

☐ _____   ☐ _____

Session Notes

Session Notes

Combat Notes & Stat Blocks

SESSION

Game Date: _____

World Date: _____

Pregame

☐ _____   ☐ _____
☐ _____   ☐ _____
☐ _____   ☐ _____

Session Notes

_____

_____

_____

_____

_____

_____

_____

_____

_____

_____

_____

_____

_____

_____

_____

_____

_____

_____

_____

_____

_____

_____

_____

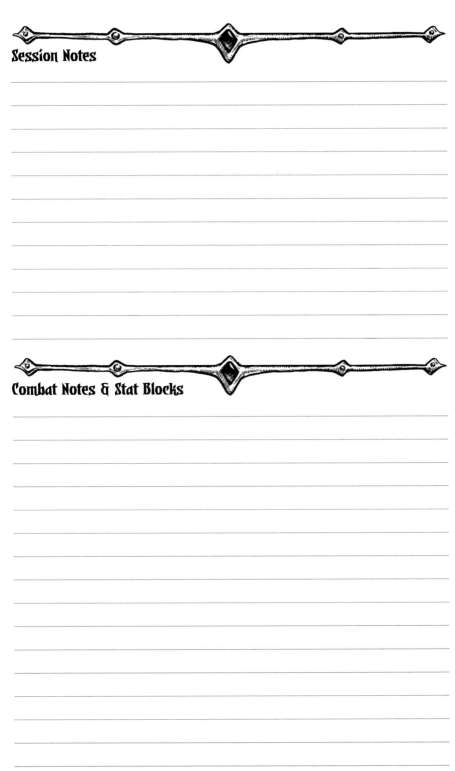

Session Notes

Combat Notes & Stat Blocks

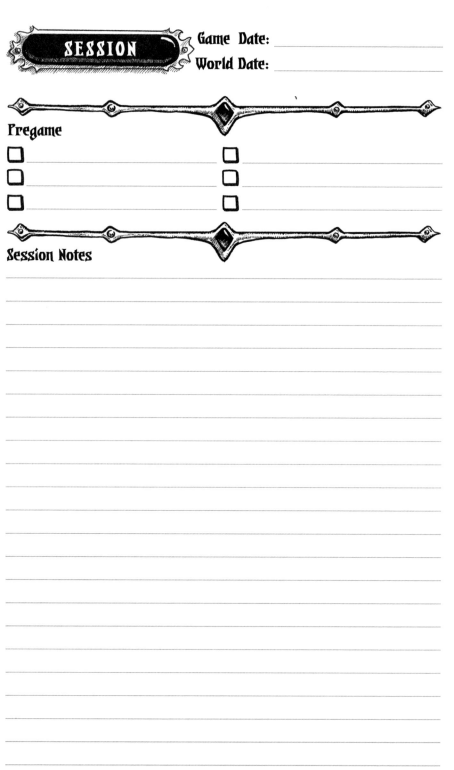

SESSION

Game Date: _____

World Date: _____

Pregame

☐ _____ ☐ _____

☐ _____ ☐ _____

☐ _____ ☐ _____

Session Notes

_____

_____

_____

_____

_____

_____

_____

_____

_____

_____

_____

_____

_____

_____

_____

_____

_____

_____

_____

_____

_____

_____

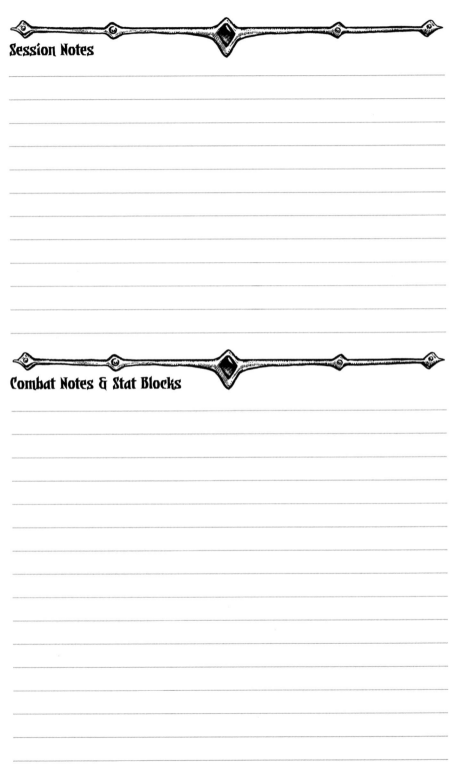

Session Notes

Combat Notes & Stat Blocks

SESSION

Game Date: _____

World Date: _____

Pregame

☐ _____   ☐ _____

☐ _____   ☐ _____

☐ _____   ☐ _____

Session Notes

_____

_____

_____

_____

_____

_____

_____

_____

_____

_____

_____

_____

_____

_____

_____

_____

_____

_____

_____

_____

_____

_____

_____

Session Notes

_____
_____
_____
_____
_____
_____
_____
_____
_____
_____
_____

Combat Notes & Stat Blocks

_____
_____
_____
_____
_____
_____
_____
_____
_____
_____
_____
_____
_____
_____
_____

SESSION

Game Date: _____

World Date: _____

Pregame

- [ ] _____
- [ ] _____
- [ ] _____
- [ ] _____
- [ ] _____
- [ ] _____

Session Notes

_____

_____

_____

_____

_____

_____

_____

_____

_____

_____

_____

_____

_____

_____

_____

_____

_____

_____

_____

_____

_____

_____

Session Notes

Combat Notes & Stat Blocks

SESSION

Game Date: _____

World Date: _____

Pregame

☐ _____ ☐ _____

☐ _____ ☐ _____

☐ _____ ☐ _____

Session Notes

_____

_____

_____

_____

_____

_____

_____

_____

_____

_____

_____

_____

_____

_____

_____

_____

_____

_____

_____

_____

_____

_____

Session Notes

Combat Notes & Stat Blocks

SESSION

Game Date: _____

World Date: _____

Pregame

☐ _____ ☐ _____

☐ _____ ☐ _____

☐ _____ ☐ _____

Session Notes

_____

_____

_____

_____

_____

_____

_____

_____

_____

_____

_____

_____

_____

_____

_____

_____

_____

_____

_____

_____

_____

Session Notes

Combat Notes & Stat Blocks

SESSION

Game Date: _____

World Date: _____

Pregame

- [ ] _____
- [ ] _____
- [ ] _____
- [ ] _____
- [ ] _____
- [ ] _____

Session Notes

_____

_____

_____

_____

_____

_____

_____

_____

_____

_____

_____

_____

_____

_____

_____

_____

_____

_____

_____

_____

_____

_____

Session Notes

Combat Notes & Stat Blocks

SESSION

Game Date: _____

World Date: _____

Pregame

- [ ] _____
- [ ] _____
- [ ] _____
- [ ] _____
- [ ] _____
- [ ] _____

Session Notes

_____

_____

_____

_____

_____

_____

_____

_____

_____

_____

_____

_____

_____

_____

_____

_____

_____

_____

_____

_____

_____

_____

_____

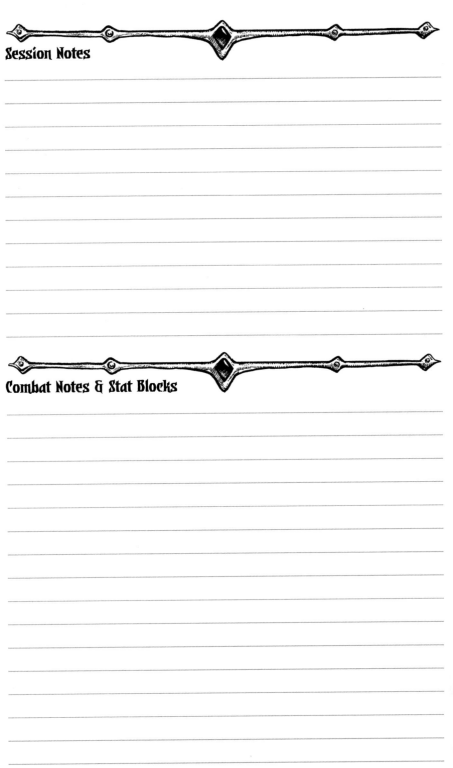

Session Notes

Combat Notes & Stat Blocks

SESSION

Game Date: _____

World Date: _____

Pregame

☐ _____   ☐ _____
☐ _____   ☐ _____
☐ _____   ☐ _____

Session Notes

_____
_____
_____
_____
_____
_____
_____
_____
_____
_____
_____
_____
_____
_____
_____
_____
_____
_____
_____
_____
_____
_____

Session Notes

Combat Notes & Stat Blocks

SESSION

Game Date: _____

World Date: _____

Pregame

☐ _____   ☐ _____

☐ _____   ☐ _____

☐ _____   ☐ _____

Session Notes

Session Notes

Combat Notes & Stat Blocks

SESSION

Game Date: _____

World Date: _____

Pregame

☐ _____   ☐ _____

☐ _____   ☐ _____

☐ _____   ☐ _____

Session Notes

_____

_____

_____

_____

_____

_____

_____

_____

_____

_____

_____

_____

_____

_____

_____

_____

_____

_____

_____

_____

_____

_____

_____

_____

_____

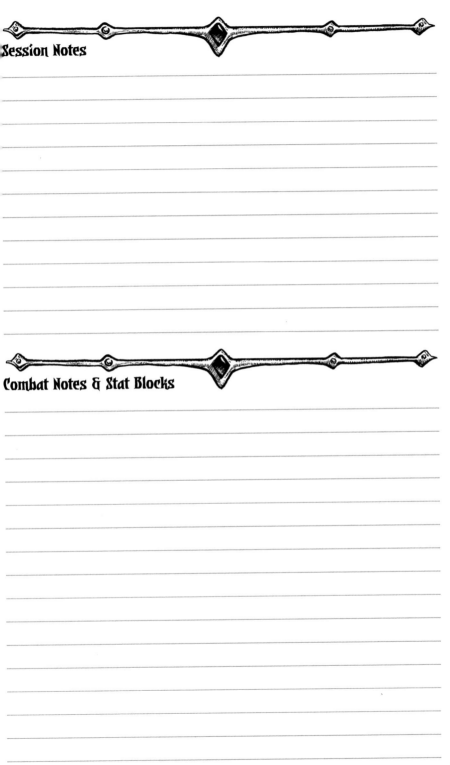

Session Notes

Combat Notes & Stat Blocks

SESSION

Game Date: _____

World Date: _____

Pregame

☐ _____   ☐ _____
☐ _____   ☐ _____
☐ _____   ☐ _____

Session Notes

_____

_____

_____

_____

_____

_____

_____

_____

_____

_____

_____

_____

_____

_____

_____

_____

_____

_____

_____

_____

_____

_____

_____

_____

_____

Session Notes

Combat Notes & Stat Blocks

SESSION

Game Date: _____

World Date: _____

Pregame

☐ _____   ☐ _____
☐ _____   ☐ _____
☐ _____   ☐ _____

Session Notes

_____

_____

_____

_____

_____

_____

_____

_____

_____

_____

_____

_____

_____

_____

_____

_____

_____

_____

_____

_____

Session Notes

Combat Notes & Stat Blocks

SESSION

Game Date: _____

World Date: _____

Pregame

☐ _____   ☐ _____

☐ _____   ☐ _____

☐ _____   ☐ _____

Session Notes

_____

_____

_____

_____

_____

_____

_____

_____

_____

_____

_____

_____

_____

_____

_____

_____

_____

_____

_____

_____

_____

_____

_____

_____

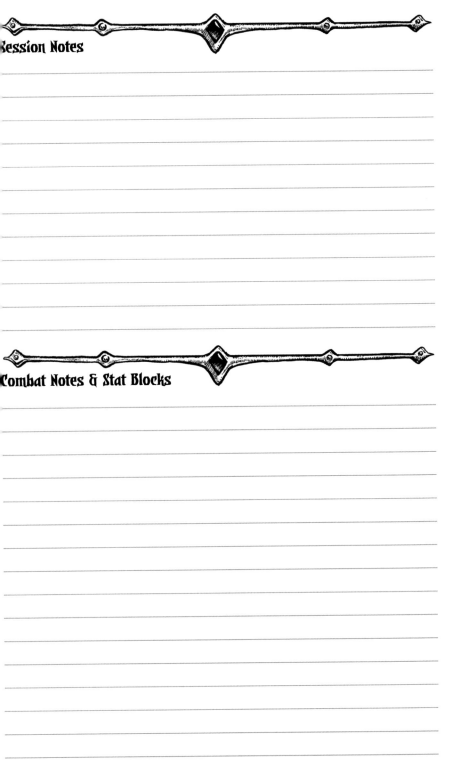

Session Notes

Combat Notes & Stat Blocks

SESSION

Game Date: _____

World Date: _____

Pregame

☐ _____   ☐ _____

☐ _____   ☐ _____

☐ _____   ☐ _____

Session Notes

Session Notes

Combat Notes & Stat Blocks

SESSION

Game Date: _____

World Date: _____

Pregame

☐ _____   ☐ _____
☐ _____   ☐ _____
☐ _____   ☐ _____

Session Notes

_____
_____
_____
_____
_____
_____
_____
_____
_____
_____
_____
_____
_____
_____
_____
_____
_____
_____
_____
_____
_____
_____
_____
_____

Session Notes

Combat Notes & Stat Blocks

CHARACTERS

Name: _____

Campaign: _____

Player Characters

People, Places, & Things

NOTES